SUPERHERO BUNNY LEAGUE

IN SPACE!

Written and illustrated by

Jamie Smart

In their first adventure, the SUPERHERO BUNNY LEAGUE
beat the wicked Doctor Fuzzleglove. They went on to defeat
many other DANGEROUS enemies ...

OXFORD

UNIVERSITY PRESS

OXFORD
UNIVERSITY PRESS

Great Clarendon Street, Oxford, OX2 6DP, United Kingdom

Oxford University Press is a department of the University
of Oxford. It furthers the University's objective of excellence
in research, scholarship, and education by publishing
worldwide. Oxford is a registered trade mark of Oxford
University Press in the UK and in certain other countries

Text and illustrations © Fumboo Limited 2015

The moral rights of the author have been asserted

First published 2015

British Library Cataloguing in Publication Data
Data available

ISBN: 978-0-19-835664-6

10 9 8 7 6 5

Paper used in the production of this book is a natural, recyclable product
made from wood grown in sustainable forests. The manufacturing process
conforms to the environmental regulations of the country of origin.

Printed in China by Golden Cup

Acknowledgements

Series Advisor: Nikki Gamble

STUMPY

He turns into liquid when
he gets embarrassed!

HANDSOME STEVE

He's super-strong!

DEREK

He grows HUGE when
he's angry!

WINDY

She flies like the wind!

3

9

24

25

27